The Really Easy Uke Book

© 2009 by Faber Music Ltd
First published by Faber Music Ltd in 2009
Bloomsbury House 74–77 Great Russell Street London WC1B 3DA

Arranged by Alex Davis
Edited by Lucy Holliday

Designed by Lydia Merrills-Ashcroft
Photography by Ben Turner

Special thanks to Alex & Helen, Caroline, David, Eleanor, Hannah,
Henry, Janella & Rachel.

Printed in England by Caligraving Ltd

The text paper used in this publication is a virgin fibre product that
is manufactured in the UK to ISO 14001 standards. The wood fibre
used is only sourced from managed forests using sustainable
forestry principles. This paper is 100% recyclable

ISBN10: 0-571-53374-4
EAN13: 978-0-571-53374-9

To buy Faber Music publications or to find out about the full range
of titles available, please contact your local music retailer or
Faber Music sales enquiries:

Faber Music Ltd, Burnt Mill, Elizabeth Way,
Harlow, CM20 2HX England
Tel: +44(0)1279 82 89 82
Fax: +44(0)1279 82 89 83
sales@fabermusic.com fabermusic.com

All Along The Watchtower 08

Amazing Grace 09

Danny Boy 11

Delilah 12

Dirty Old Town 15

Early One Morning 16

Edelweiss 17

Get Me To The Church On Time 20

Greased Lightnin' 18

Happy Birthday To You 23

The Hippopotamus Song 24

The House Of The Rising Sun 26

How Much Is That Doggie In The Window? 28

I Do Like To Be Beside The Seaside 10

I Have A Dream 30

I Wanna Be Like You 36

If I Had A Hammer 33

(Is This The Way To) Amarillo? 38

It's In His Kiss (Shoop, Shoop Song) 52

Knees Up Mother Brown 40

Kum Ba Yah 41

Little Brown Jug 42

My Grandfather's Clock 46

Over The Rainbow 56

Proud Mary 48

Rock Around The Clock 43

Shake, Rattle And Roll 50

The Skye Boat Song 54

Sloop John B 55

Supercalifragilisticexpialidocious 58

This Old Man 61

When I'm Cleaning Windows 62

When The Saints Go Marching In 65

Whiskey In The Jar 66

Y Viva España 67

Yankee Doodle 68

Tuning

The standard Ukulele string tuning is G–C–E–A, shown here on the treble stave and piano keyboard. Note that the G string is tuned higher than the C string.

You can tune your Ukulele using a piano or keyboard (or any other instrument that you know is in tune!) or by using an electronic chromatic tuner.

If just one string on your Ukulele is in tune then you can use it to tune the other strings as well.

This diagram shows which fretted notes match the note of the open string above. Eg. Pluck the first string at the 5th fret and match the note to the second open string, and so on.

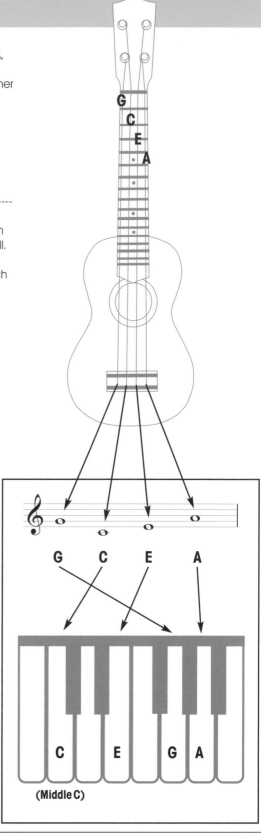

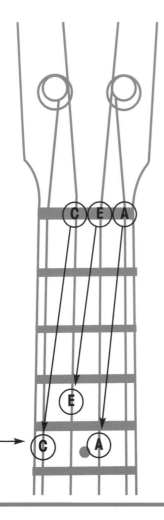

(Sounds an octave higher)

G   C   E   A

C   E   G   A

(Middle C)

Reading Chord Boxes

A chord box is basically a diagram of how a chord is played on the neck of the Ukulele. It shows you which string to play, where to put your fingers and whereabouts on the neck the chord is played.

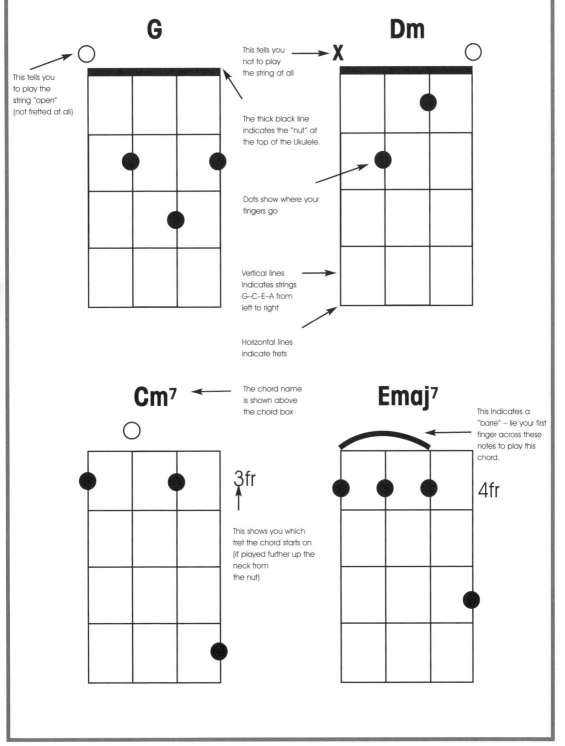

G

This tells you to play the string "open" (not fretted at all)

Dm

This tells you not to play the string at all **X**

The thick black line indicates the "nut" at the top of the Ukulele.

Dots show where your fingers go

Vertical lines indicates strings G–C–E–A from left to right

Horizontal lines indicate frets

Cm⁷

The chord name is shown above the chord box

Emaj⁷

This indicates a "barre" – lie your first finger across these notes to play this chord.

3fr

This shows you which fret the chord starts on (if played further up the neck from the nut)

4fr

The academic point-of-view...

Ukulele: (pronounced Yoo-Ka-Lay-Lee) of Hawaiian origin, occasionally abbreviated as the uke, is a "chordophone classified as a plucked lute; it is a subset of the guitar family of instruments, generally with four nylon or gut strings or four courses of strings."

Erich M. von Hornbostel & Curt Sachs, *Classification of Musical Instruments*: Translated from the Original German by Anthony Baines and Klaus P. Wachsmann. The Galpin Society Journal 14, 1961: 3-29

The thoughtful point-of-view...

"The ukulele...the thinking man's violin"

Krusty the Clown, entertainer and philosopher from *The Simpsons*.

History of the Ukulele

Whatever point of view you take, one thing you can't ignore about the Ukulele is that it's fun. It originally comes from Hawaii which is, after all, a pretty fun place. To be even more exact it arrived in Honolulu aboard a ship called the Ravenscrag, carrying 419 Portuguese immigrants from the island of Madeira to work in the sugar cane fields, on the afternoon of August 23, 1879. To alleviate boredom during the long Atlantic sea journey these newcomers had brought with them a few small, four stringed, fretted instruments known as a **Machete de Braga** (sometimes known as a **Machete** or **Braguinha**, a smaller but similar instrument to the modern Cavaquinho) which immediately captured the imagination and hearts of the native Hawaiians – not least of all their King Kalakaua who ended up incorporating Ukulele performances into Royal gatherings! His successor, Queen Lili'uokalani, believed that the word 'Ukulele' meant "the gift that came here" from the Hawaiian words **uku** (gift or reward) and **lele** (to come), although there are many other theories.

Three of the newcomers had been cabinet makers back in Maderira and had no difficulty in transferring their skills to Ukulele manufacture by the mid-1880s. Things must have gone crazy from that point – by the time Hawaii had joined the United States in 1900 the Ukulele was by far and away the islands most popular instrument. The Hawaiian exhibit at the Panama-Pacific International Exposition of 1915 did much to open American eyes to this island of sunshine and Ukuleles, and it didn't take long for Hollywood studios and Tin Pan Alley songwriters to start using the instrument in films and songs. Stars such as Cliff Edwards in the US and George Formby in the UK helped popularise the Ukulele beyond even the guitar, (sheet music from the '20s and '30s generally features Uke chords!), and mainstream instrument manufacturers such as Martin and Gibson were knocking out thousands of them.

The Ukulele has had its ups and downs since then – the Great Depression saw a fall in popularity, followed by renewed interest after the 2nd World War, helped by Maccaferri's manufacture of cheap plastic Ukes, television performances by Arthur Godfrey and the memorable recordings of Tiny Tim. Things tailed off again by the end of the '60s - rock'n'roll had placed the guitar at the forefront of the popular musicians arsenal and the social/political unrest surrounding things like the Vietnam war didn't really go hand-in-hand with the cheerful sound of the Uke. Things changed yet again in the '90s with all kinds of musicians around the world bringing the instrument back into the public eye (ranging from traditional Hawaiian artists like Israel Kamakawiwo'ole to the Ukulele Orchestra Of Great Britain, not to mention a good few Indie bands), many new manufacturers bringing out Ukes at prices to suit everyone, and the likes of George Harrison and Paul McCartney singing the praises of the Ukulele to us all.

ALL ALONG THE WATCHTOWER

Words and Music by Bob Dylan

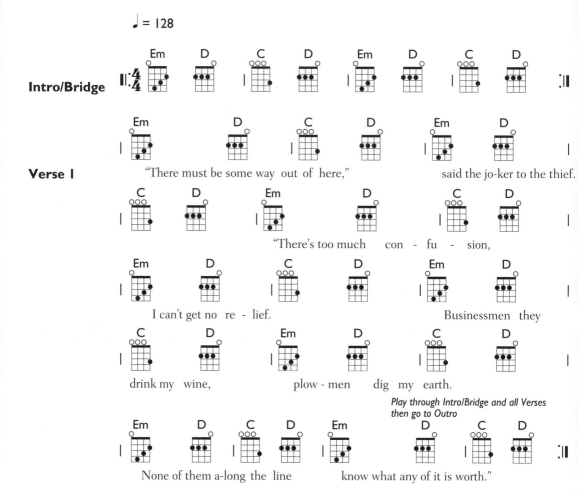

Intro/Bridge

Verse 1

"There must be some way out of here," said the jo-ker to the thief.

"There's too much con - fu - sion,

I can't get no re - lief. Businessmen they

drink my wine, plow - men dig my earth.

Play through Intro/Bridge and all Verses then go to Outro

None of them a-long the line know what any of it is worth."

Verse 2

"No reason to get excited", the thief he kindly spoke,
"There are many here among us who feel that life is but a joke.
But you and I, we've been through that, and this is not our fate,
So let us not talk falsely now, the hour is getting late. "

Verse 3

All along the watchtower, princes kept the view
While all the women came and went, barefoot servants, too.
Outside in the distance a wildcat did growl,
Two riders were approaching, the wind began to howl.

Outro

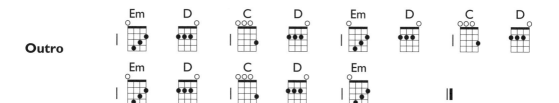

AMAZING GRACE
Traditional

♩ = 70

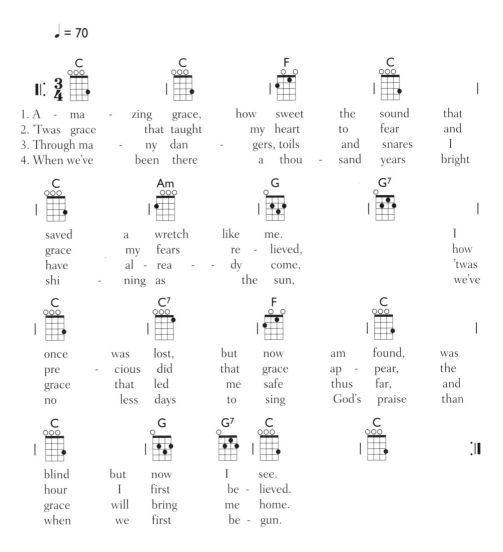

Verses

	C	C	F	C
1.	A - ma - zing grace,	how sweet	the sound	that
2.	'Twas grace that taught	my heart	to fear	and
3.	Through ma - ny dan - gers, toils	and snares	I
4.	When we've been there	a thou - sand years	bright

C	Am	G	G⁷
saved	a wretch	like me.	I
grace	my fears	re - lieved,	how
have	al - rea - dy	come,	'twas
shi - ning as	the sun,	we've

C	C⁷	F	C
once was lost,	but now	am found,	was
pre - cious did	that grace	ap - pear,	the
grace that led	me safe	thus far,	and
no less days	to sing	God's praise	than

C	G	G⁷ C	C
blind	but now	I see.	
hour	I	first	be - lieved.
grace	will	bring	me home.
when	we	first	be - gun.

Trad.

I DO LIKE TO BE BESIDE THE SEASIDE

Words and Music by John A. Glover-Kind

♩ = 125

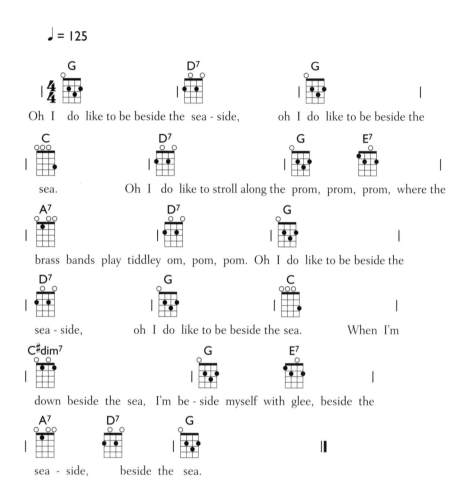

G	D⁷	G	

Oh I do like to be beside the sea - side,   oh I do like to be beside the

C	D⁷	G	E⁷	

sea.   Oh I do like to stroll along the prom, prom, prom, where the

A⁷	D⁷	G	

brass bands play tiddley om, pom, pom. Oh I do like to be beside the

D⁷	G	C	

sea - side,   oh I do like to be beside the sea.   When I'm

C#dim⁷	G	E⁷	

down beside the sea, I'm be - side myself with glee, beside the

A⁷	D⁷	G	

sea - side,   beside the sea.

DANNY BOY

Words by Frederick Weatherly
Music Traditional

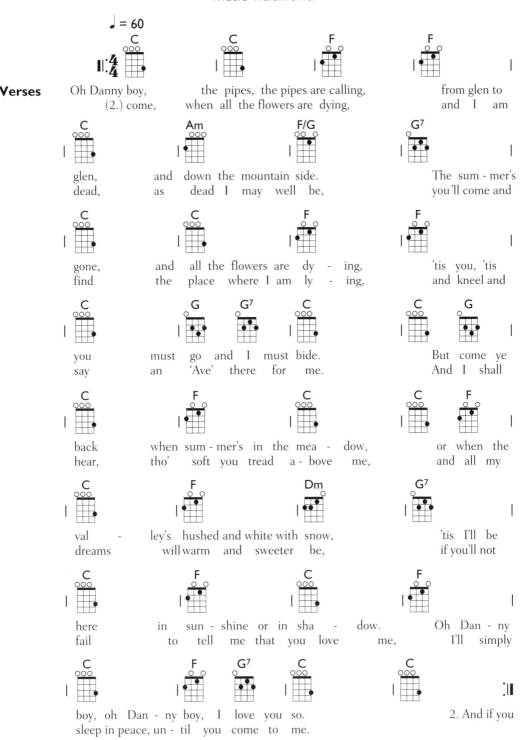

Verses

Oh Danny boy, the pipes, the pipes are calling, from glen to
(2.) come, when all the flowers are dying, and I am

glen, and down the mountain side. The sum - mer's
dead, as dead I may well be, you'll come and

gone, and all the flowers are dy - ing, 'tis you, 'tis
find the place where I am ly - ing, and kneel and

you must go and I must bide. But come ye
say an 'Ave' there for me. And I shall

back when sum - mer's in the mea - dow, or when the
hear, tho' soft you tread a - bove me, and all my

val - ley's hushed and white with snow, 'tis I'll be
dreams will warm and sweeter be, if you'll not

here in sun - shine or in sha - dow. Oh Dan - ny
fail to tell me that you love me, I'll simply

boy, oh Dan - ny boy, I love you so.
sleep in peace, un - til you come to me.

2. And if you

DELILAH

Words and Music by Les Reed and Barry Mason

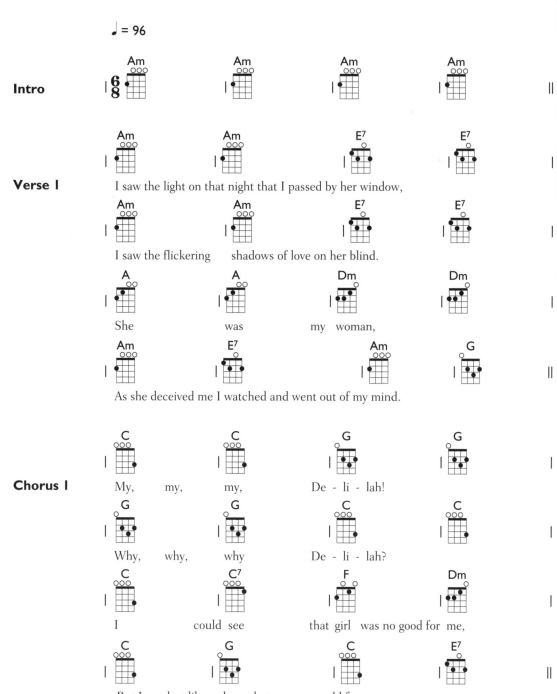

♩ = 96

Intro — Am / Am / Am / Am

Verse 1

Am / Am / E⁷ / E⁷
I saw the light on that night that I passed by her window,

Am / Am / E⁷ / E⁷
I saw the flickering   shadows of love on her blind.

A / A / Dm / Dm
She   was   my   woman,

Am / E⁷ / Am / G
As she deceived me I watched and went out of my mind.

Chorus 1

C / C / G / G
My,   my,   my,   De - li - lah!

G / G / C / C
Why,   why,   why   De - li - lah?

C / C⁷ / F / Dm
I   could   see   that girl   was no good for me,

C / G / C / E⁷
But I was lost like a slave   that no man could free.

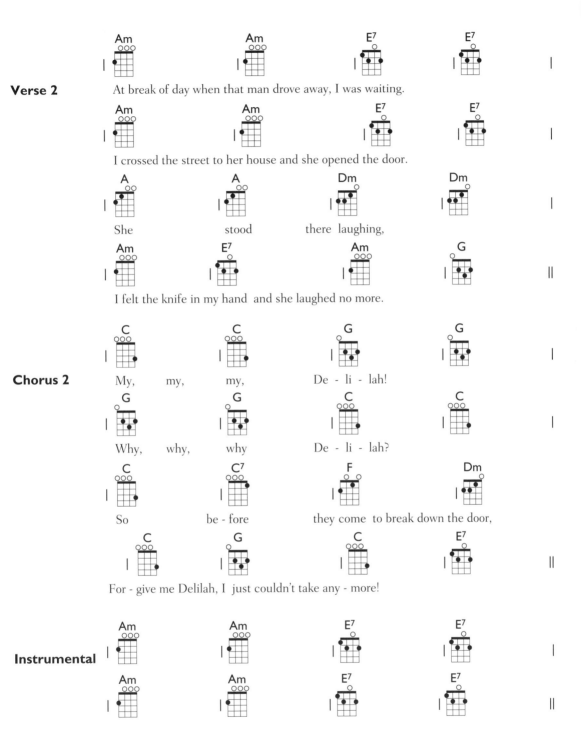

Verse 2 At break of day when that man drove away, I was waiting.

I crossed the street to her house and she opened the door.

She stood there laughing,

I felt the knife in my hand and she laughed no more.

Chorus 2 My, my, my, De - li - lah!

Why, why, why De - li - lah?

So be - fore they come to break down the door,

For - give me Delilah, I just couldn't take any - more!

Instrumental

14

Bridge

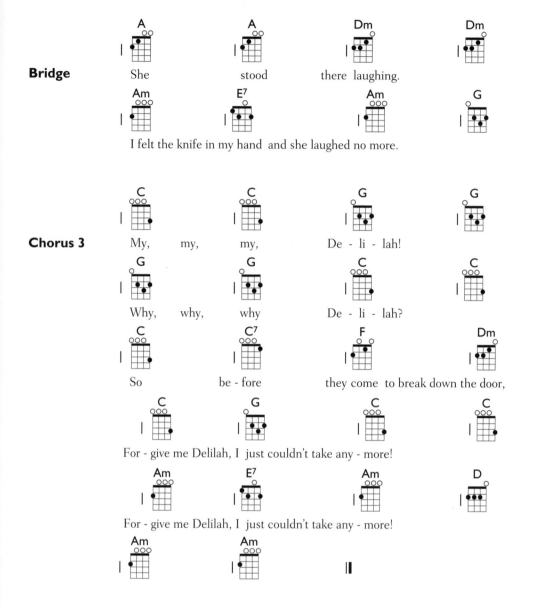

A · A · Dm · Dm

She stood there laughing.

Am · E⁷ · Am · G

I felt the knife in my hand and she laughed no more.

Chorus 3

C · C · G · G

My, my, my, De - li - lah!

G · G · C · C

Why, why, why De - li - lah?

C · C⁷ · F · Dm

So be - fore they come to break down the door,

C · G · C · C

For - give me Delilah, I just couldn't take any - more!

Am · E⁷ · Am · D

For - give me Delilah, I just couldn't take any - more!

Am · Am

DIRTY OLD TOWN

Words and Music by Ewan MacColl

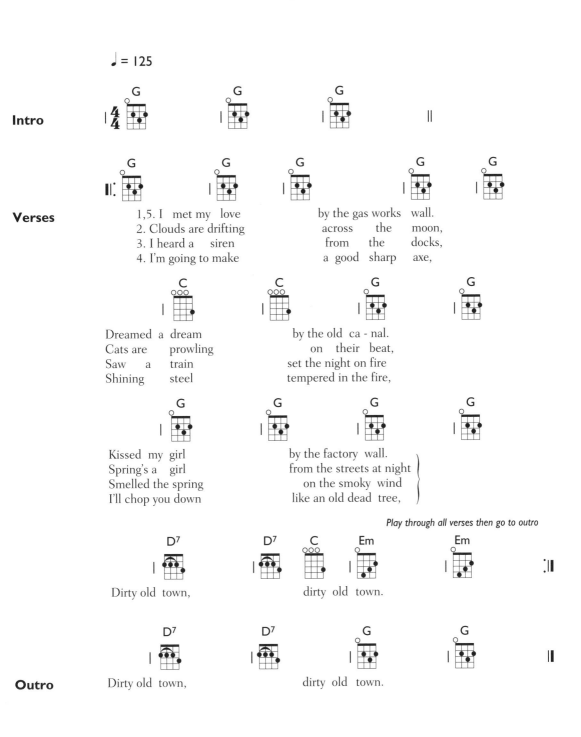

Intro

Verses

1,5. I met my love — by the gas works wall.
2. Clouds are drifting — across the moon,
3. I heard a siren — from the docks,
4. I'm going to make — a good sharp axe,

Dreamed a dream — by the old ca - nal.
Cats are prowling — on their beat,
Saw a train — set the night on fire
Shining steel — tempered in the fire,

Kissed my girl — by the factory wall.
Spring's a girl — from the streets at night
Smelled the spring — on the smoky wind
I'll chop you down — like an old dead tree,

Play through all verses then go to outro

Dirty old town, — dirty old town.

Outro

Dirty old town, — dirty old town.

Trad.

EARLY ONE MORNING

Traditional

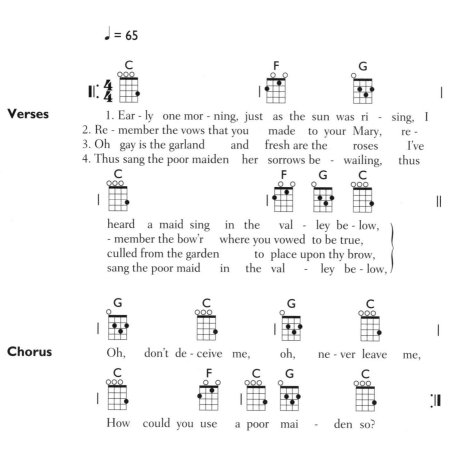

♩ = 65

Verses

|C| |F| |G| |

1. Ear - ly one mor - ning, just as the sun was ri - sing, I
2. Re - member the vows that you made to your Mary, re -
3. Oh gay is the garland and fresh are the roses I've
4. Thus sang the poor maiden her sorrows be - wailing, thus

|C| |F| |G| |C| |

heard a maid sing in the val - ley be - low,
- member the bow'r where you vowed to be true,
culled from the garden to place upon thy brow,
sang the poor maid in the val - ley be - low,

|G| |C| |G| |C| |

Chorus

Oh, don't de - ceive me, oh, ne - ver leave me,

|C| |F| |C| |G| |C| |

How could you use a poor mai - den so?

This arrangement © 2009 Faber Music Ltd

EDELWEISS
(FROM "THE SOUND OF MUSIC")

Lyrics by Oscar Hammerstein II
Music by Richard Rodgers

♩ = 103

GREASED LIGHTNIN'
(FROM "GREASE")

Words and Music by Jim Jacobs and Warren Casey

♩ = 150

Verses

1. We'll get some overhead lifters and four barrel quads, oh yeah. *Keep talkin',*
(2.) purple fringe tail-lights and thirty inch fins, oh yeah.

whoa keep talkin'. Fuel injection cutoffs and chrome plated rods, oh yeah
A Palomino dashboard and duel muffler twins, oh yea

We'll get it ready, I'll kill to get it ready. With a four-speed on the floor, they'll be
With new pistons, plugs and shocks, I can

waitin' at the door. You know that ain't no s***, we'll be gettin' lots of tit in Greased
get off my rocks, you know that I ain't bragging, she's a real pussy wagon, Grease

Light - ning. *Light - ning, go, go, go, go, go, go, go, go.*

Chorus

Go Greased Lightning, you're burning up the quarter mile. *Greased Lightning,*

Go Greased Lightning. Go Greased Lightning, you're coastin' through the heat lap tria

You are su - preme, the chicks'll
Greased Lightning, go Greased Lightning. Uh! Uh!

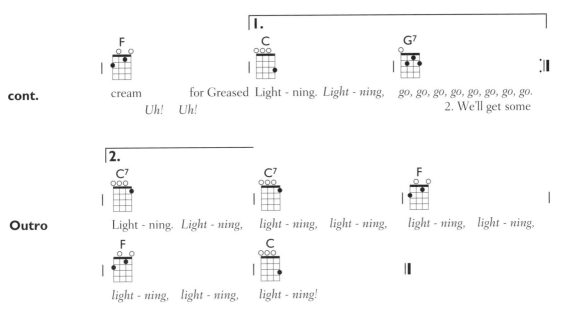

cont.

1.

F — cream   C — for Greased Light - ning. *Light - ning,*   G⁷ — *go, go, go, go, go, go, go, go.*

Uh!   *Uh!*   2. We'll get some

Outro

2.

C⁷ — Light - ning. *Light - ning,*   C⁷ — *light - ning,*   *light - ning,*   F — *light - ning,*   *light - ning,*

F — *light - ning,*   *light - ning,*   C — *light - ning!*

GET ME TO THE CHURCH ON TIME
(FROM "MY FAIR LADY")

Words by Alan Jay Lerner

Music by Frederick Loewe

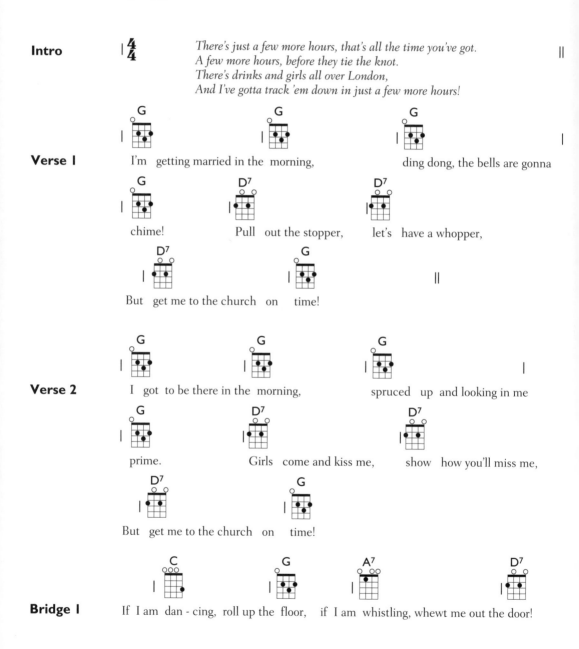

♩ = 115

Intro

| 4/4

There's just a few more hours, that's all the time you've got.
A few more hours, before they tie the knot.
There's drinks and girls all over London,
And I've gotta track 'em down in just a few more hours!

Verse 1

G   G   G

I'm getting married in the morning,   ding dong, the bells are gonna

G   D7   D7

chime!   Pull out the stopper,   let's have a whopper,

D7   G

But get me to the church on time!

Verse 2

G   G   G

I got to be there in the morning,   spruced up and looking in me

G   D7   D7

prime.   Girls come and kiss me,   show how you'll miss me,

D7   G

But get me to the church on time!

Bridge 1

C   G   A7   D7

If I am dan - cing, roll up the floor, if I am whistling, whewt me out the door!

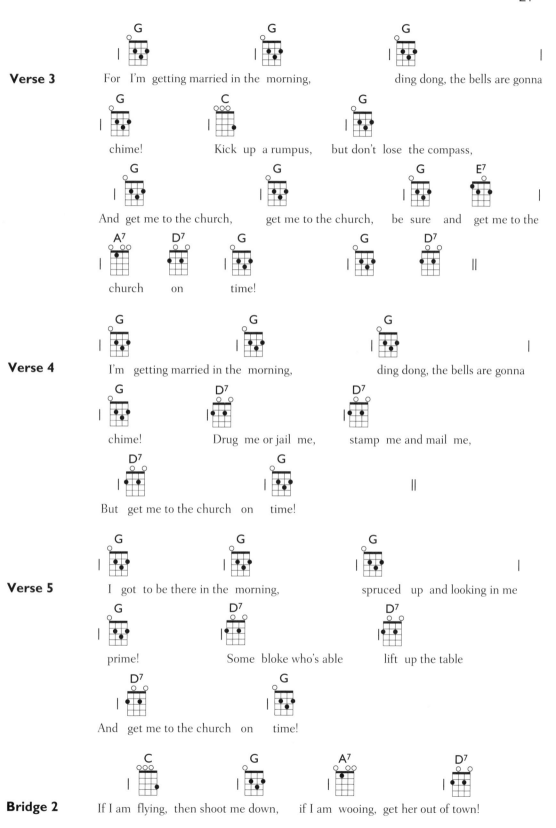

Verse 3

For I'm getting married in the morning, ding dong, the bells are gonna chime! Kick up a rumpus, but don't lose the compass, And get me to the church, get me to the church, be sure and get me to the church on time!

Verse 4

I'm getting married in the morning, ding dong, the bells are gonna chime! Drug me or jail me, stamp me and mail me, But get me to the church on time!

Verse 5

I got to be there in the morning, spruced up and looking in me prime! Some bloke who's able lift up the table And get me to the church on time!

Bridge 2

If I am flying, then shoot me down, if I am wooing, get her out of town!

Verse 6

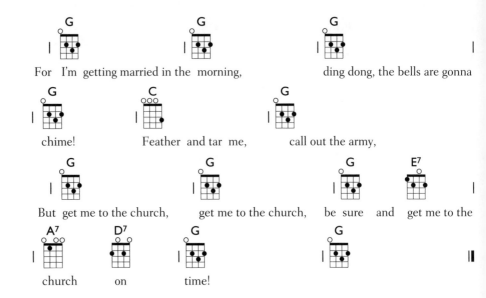

For I'm getting married in the morning, ding dong, the bells are gonna

chime! Feather and tar me, call out the army,

But get me to the church, get me to the church, be sure and get me to the

church on time!

HAPPY BIRTHDAY TO YOU

Words and Music by Patty S Hill and Mildred Hill

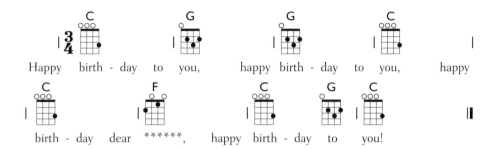

C	G	G	C	
Happy birth - day to you,	happy birth - day to you,			happy

C	F	C	G	C	
birth - day dear ******,	happy	birth - day	to	you!	

THE HIPPOPOTAMUS SONG

Words by Michael Flanders
Music by Donald Swann

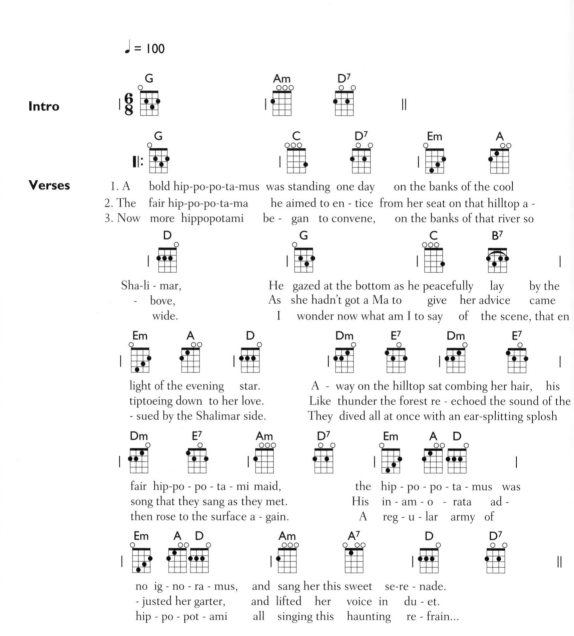

Intro

Verses

1. A bold hip-po-po-ta-mus was standing one day on the banks of the cool
2. The fair hip-po-po-ta-ma he aimed to en-tice from her seat on that hilltop a-
3. Now more hippopotami be-gan to convene, on the banks of that river so

Sha-li-mar, He gazed at the bottom as he peacefully lay by the
-bove, As she hadn't got a Ma to give her advice came
wide. I wonder now what am I to say of the scene, that en

light of the evening star. A-way on the hilltop sat combing her hair, his
tiptoeing down to her love. Like thunder the forest re-echoed the sound of the
-sued by the Shalimar side. They dived all at once with an ear-splitting splosh

fair hip-po-po-ta-mi maid, the hip-po-po-ta-mus was
song that they sang as they met. His in-am-o-rata ad-
then rose to the surface a-gain. A reg-u-lar army of

no ig-no-ra-mus, and sang her this sweet se-re-nade.
-justed her garter, and lifted her voice in du-et.
hip-po-pot-ami all singing this haunting re-frain...

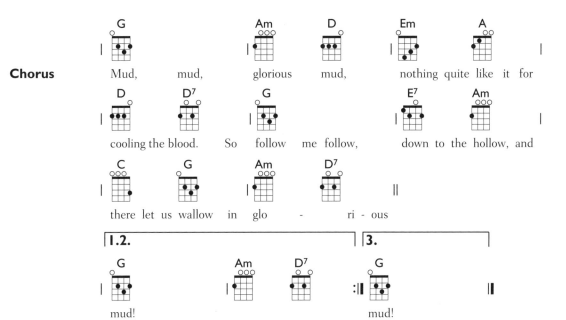

Chorus

G   Am   D   Em   A

Mud,   mud,   glorious   mud,   nothing quite like it for

D   D⁷   G   E⁷   Am

cooling the blood.   So   follow   me follow,   down to the hollow, and

C   G   Am   D⁷

there let us wallow   in   glo   -   ri - ous

1.2.   **3.**

G   Am   D⁷   G

mud!   mud!

THE HOUSE OF THE RISING SUN

Traditional

Arranged by Alan Price

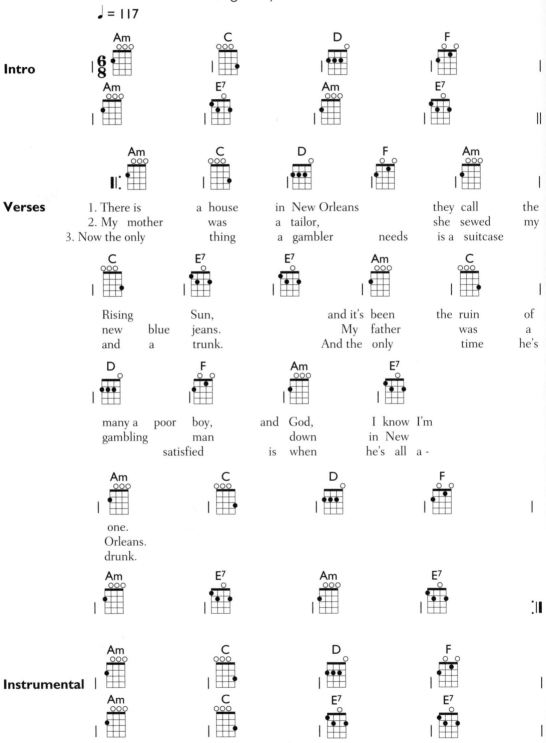

♩ = 117

Intro

Verses

1. There is a house in New Orleans they call the
2. My mother was a tailor, she sewed my
3. Now the only thing a gambler needs is a suitcase

Rising Sun, and it's been the ruin of
new blue jeans. My father was a
and a trunk. And the only time he's

many a poor boy, and God, I know I'm
gambling man down in New
satisfied is when he's all a-

one.
Orleans.
drunk.

Instrumental

cont.

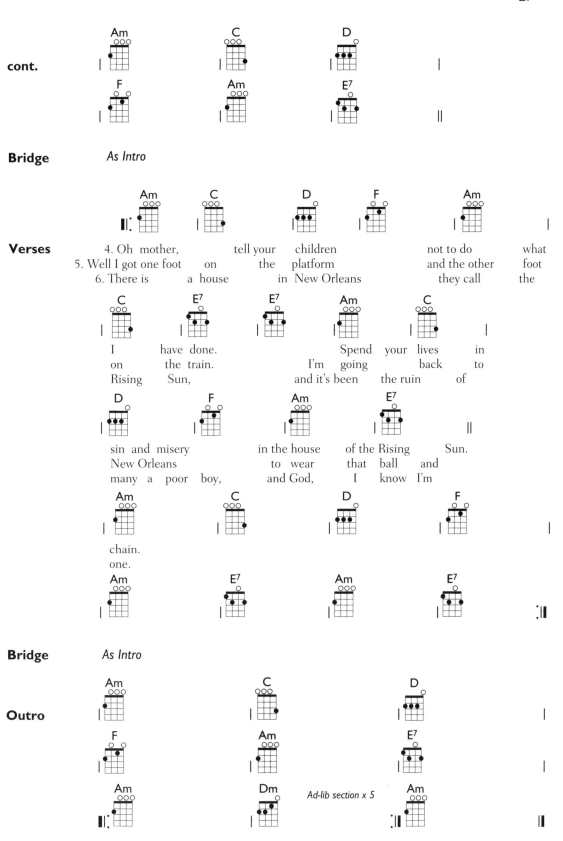

Bridge *As Intro*

Verses

4. Oh mother,   tell your   children   not to do   what
5. Well I got one foot   on   the   platform   and the other   foot
6. There is   a house   in New Orleans   they call   the

I   have done.   Spend   your   lives   in
on   the train.   I'm   going   back   to
Rising   Sun,   and it's been   the ruin   of

sin and misery   in the house   of the Rising   Sun.
New Orleans   to wear   that   ball   and
many a   poor   boy,   and God,   I   know I'm

chain.
one.

Bridge *As Intro*

Outro

Ad-lib section x 5

HOW MUCH IS THAT DOGGIE IN THE WINDOW?

Words and Music by Bob Merrill

Intro

Chorus 1 How much is that doggie in the window? The one with the waggly tail. How much is that doggie in the window? I do hope that doggie's for sale.

Verse 1 I must take a trip to Cali - fornia and leave my poor sweet-heart a - lone. If he has a dog, he won't be lonesome and the doggie will have a good home.

Chorus 2 *As Chorus 1*

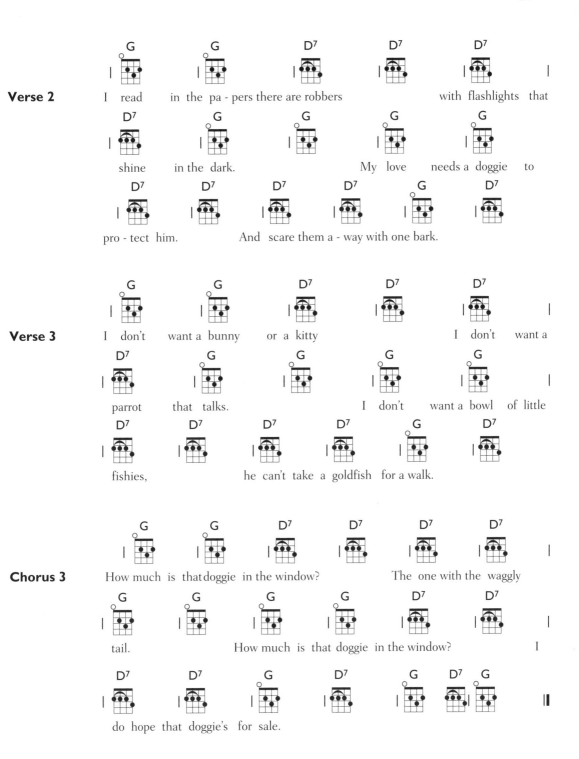

I HAVE A DREAM

Words and Music by Benny Andersson and Björn Ulvaeus

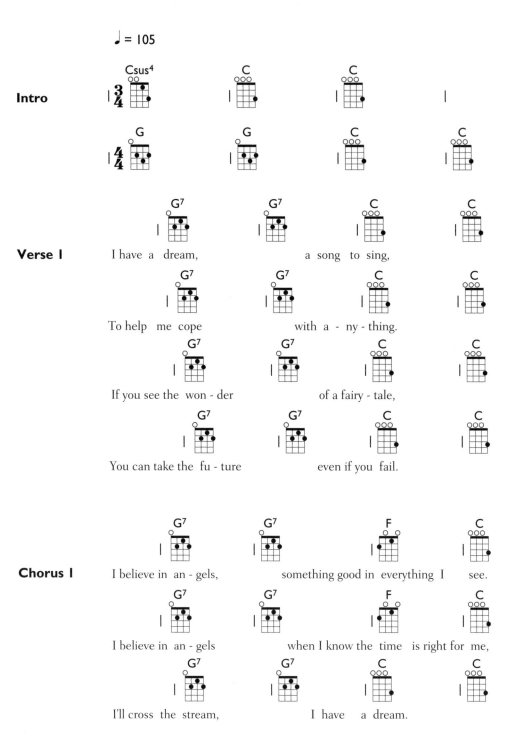

Intro

Verse 1

I have a dream, a song to sing,

To help me cope with a - ny - thing.

If you see the won - der of a fairy - tale,

You can take the fu - ture even if you fail.

Chorus 1

I believe in an - gels, something good in everything I see.

I believe in an - gels when I know the time is right for me,

I'll cross the stream, I have a dream.

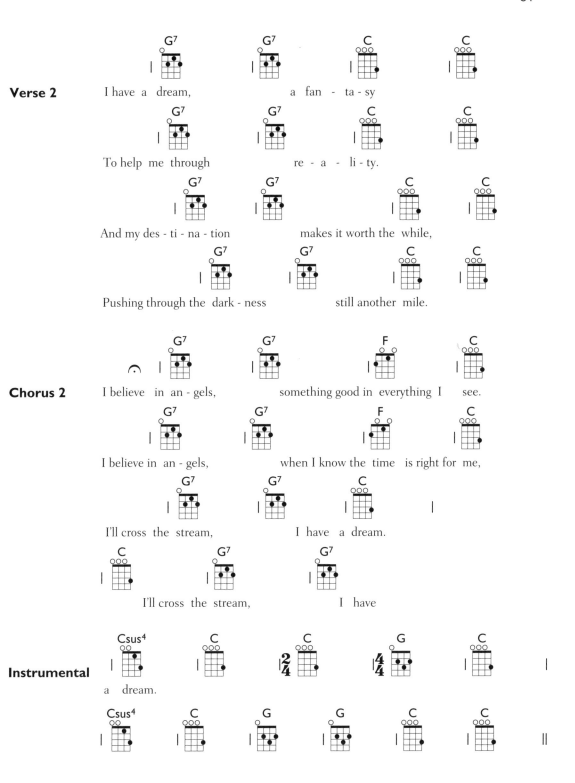

Verse 2

I have a dream, a fan - ta - sy

To help me through re - a - li - ty.

And my des - ti - na - tion makes it worth the while,

Pushing through the dark - ness still another mile.

Chorus 2

I believe in an - gels, something good in everything I see.

I believe in an - gels, when I know the time is right for me,

I'll cross the stream, I have a dream.

I'll cross the stream, I have

Instrumental

a dream.

Verse 3 *As Verse 1*

32

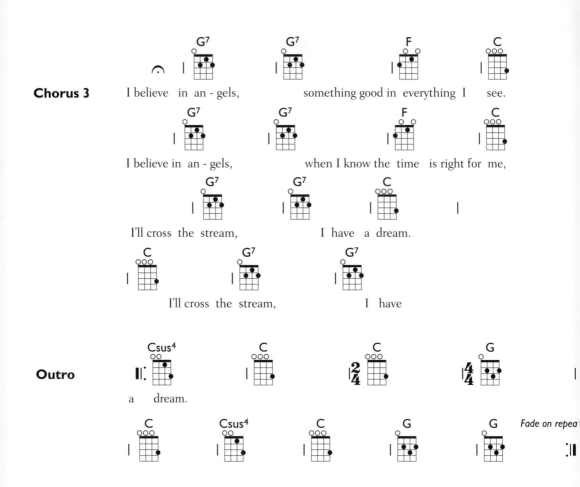

Chorus 3   I believe   in an - gels,   something good in everything I   see.

I believe in an - gels,   when I know the time   is right for me,

I'll cross the stream,   I have a dream.

I'll cross the stream,   I have

Outro   a   dream.

Fade on repeat

IF I HAD A HAMMER

Words and Music by Peter Seeger and Lee Hays

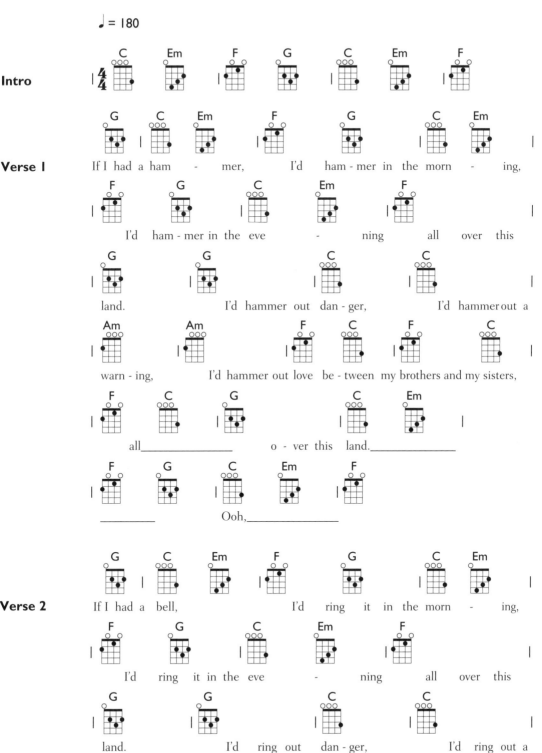

34

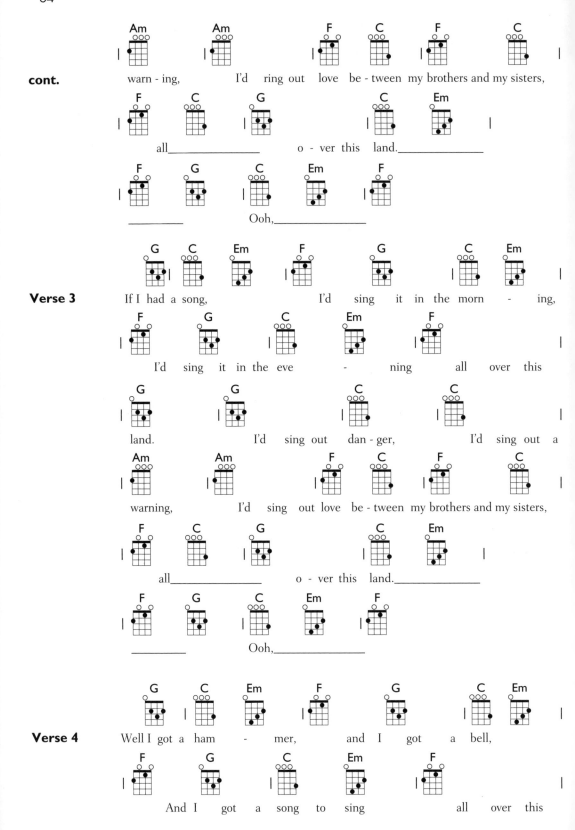

cont.

| Am | Am | | F | C | F | C |

warn - ing, I'd ring out love be - tween my brothers and my sisters,

| F | C | G | | C | Em |

all_____ o - ver this land._____

| F | G | C | Em | F |

_____ Ooh,_____

| G | C | Em | F | G | C | Em |

Verse 3 If I had a song, I'd sing it in the morn - ing,

| F | G | C | Em | F |

I'd sing it in the eve - ning all over this

| G | G | C | C |

land. I'd sing out dan - ger, I'd sing out a

| Am | Am | F | C | F | C |

warning, I'd sing out love be - tween my brothers and my sisters,

| F | C | G | | C | Em |

all_____ o - ver this land._____

| F | G | C | Em | F |

_____ Ooh,_____

| G | C | Em | F | G | C | Em |

Verse 4 Well I got a ham - mer, and I got a bell,

| F | G | C | Em | F |

And I got a song to sing all over this

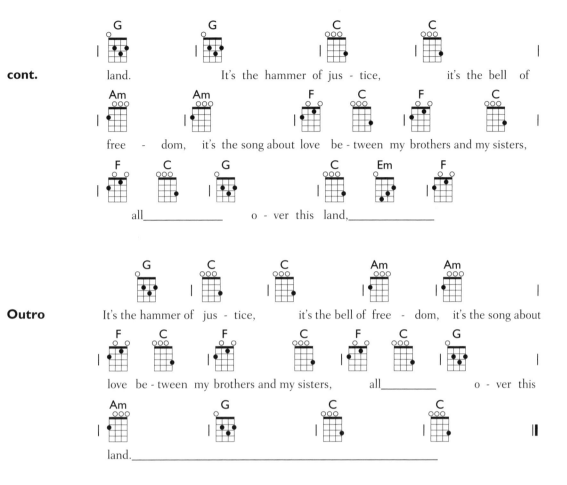

cont.

| G | G | C | C |

land. It's the hammer of jus - tice, it's the bell of

| Am | Am | F C | F C |

free - dom, it's the song about love be - tween my brothers and my sisters,

| F C | G | C Em F |

all_____ o - ver this land,_____

Outro

| G C | C | Am | Am |

It's the hammer of jus - tice, it's the bell of free - dom, it's the song about

| F C | F | C | F C | G |

love be - tween my brothers and my sisters, all_____ o - ver this

| Am | G | C | C |

land._____

I WANNA BE LIKE YOU
(FROM 'THE JUNGLE BOOK')

Words and Music by Richard Sherman and Robert Sherman

♩ = 100

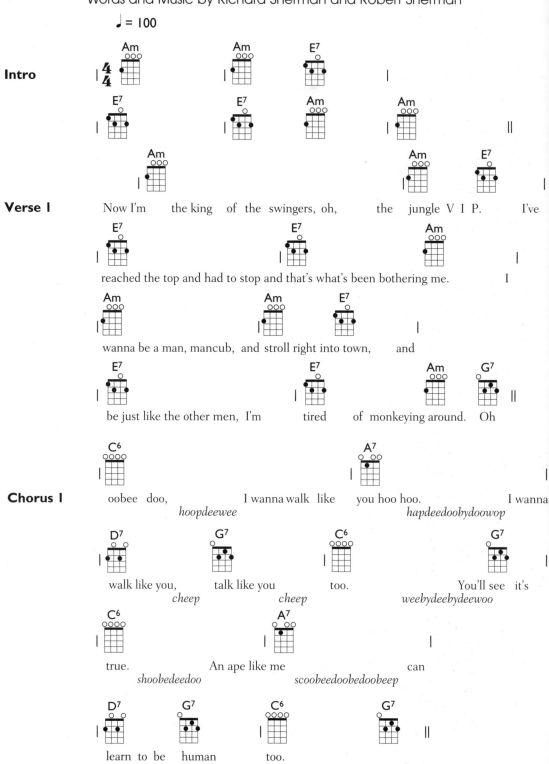

Intro

Verse I

Now I'm the king of the swingers, oh, the jungle V I P. I've

reached the top and had to stop and that's what's been bothering me. I

wanna be a man, mancub, and stroll right into town, and

be just like the other men, I'm tired of monkeying around. Oh

Chorus I

oobee doo, I wanna walk like you hoo hoo. I wanna
hoopdeewee *hapdeedooby doowop*

walk like you, talk like you too. You'll see it's
cheep *cheep* *weebydeebydeewoo*

true. An ape like me can
shoobedeedoo *scoobeedoobedoobeep*

learn to be human too.

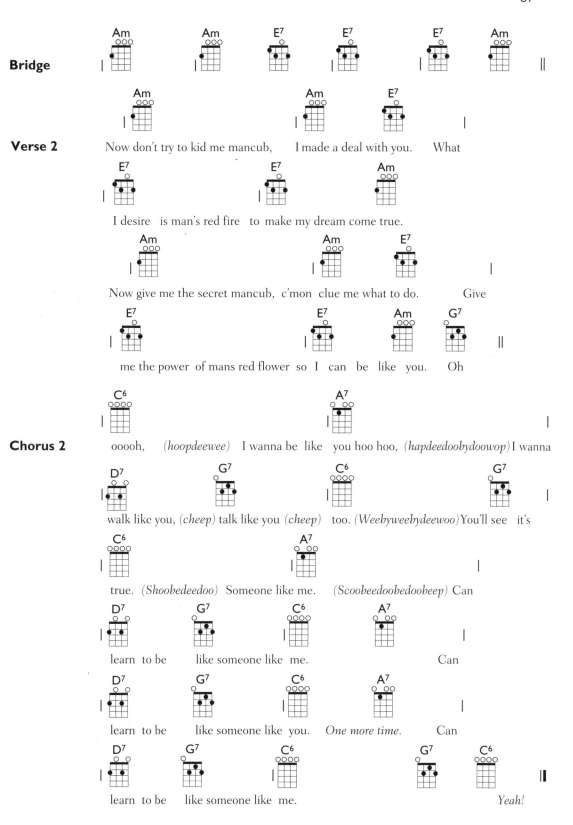

Bridge

Verse 2 Now don't try to kid me mancub, I made a deal with you. What

I desire is man's red fire to make my dream come true.

Now give me the secret mancub, c'mon clue me what to do. Give

me the power of mans red flower so I can be like you. Oh

Chorus 2 ooooh, *(hoopdeewee)* I wanna be like you hoo hoo, *(hapdeedoobydoowop)* I wanna

walk like you, *(cheep)* talk like you *(cheep)* too. *(Weebyweebydeewoo)* You'll see it's

true. *(Shoobedeedoo)* Someone like me. *(Scoobeedoobedoobeep)* Can

learn to be like someone like me. Can

learn to be like someone like you. *One more time.* Can

learn to be like someone like me. *Yeah!*

(IS THIS THE WAY TO) AMARILLO?

Words and Music by Neil Sedaka and Howard Greenfield

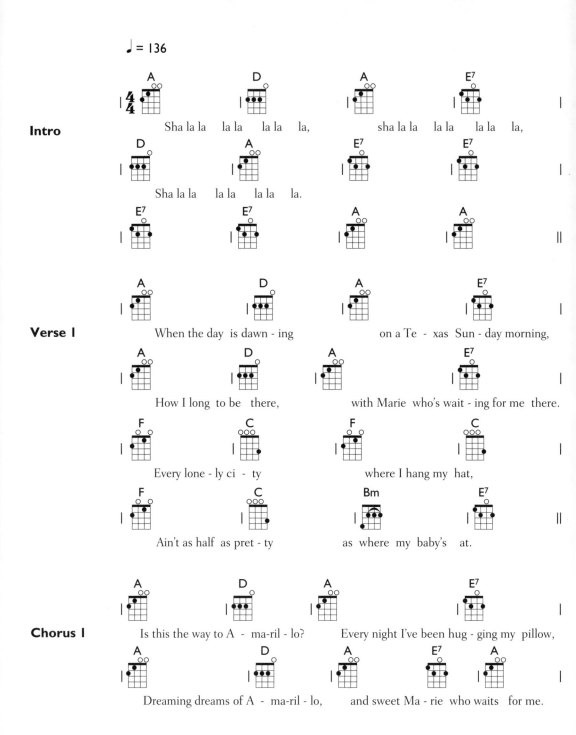

Intro

Sha la la   la la   la la la,   sha la la   la la   la la la,

Sha la la   la la   la la   la.

Verse 1

When the day is dawn - ing   on a Te - xas Sun - day morning,

How I long to be there,   with Marie who's wait - ing for me there.

Every lone - ly ci - ty   where I hang my hat,

Ain't as half as pret - ty   as where my baby's at.

Chorus 1

Is this the way to A - ma - ril - lo?   Every night I've been hug - ging my pillow,

Dreaming dreams of A - ma - ril - lo,   and sweet Ma - rie who waits for me.

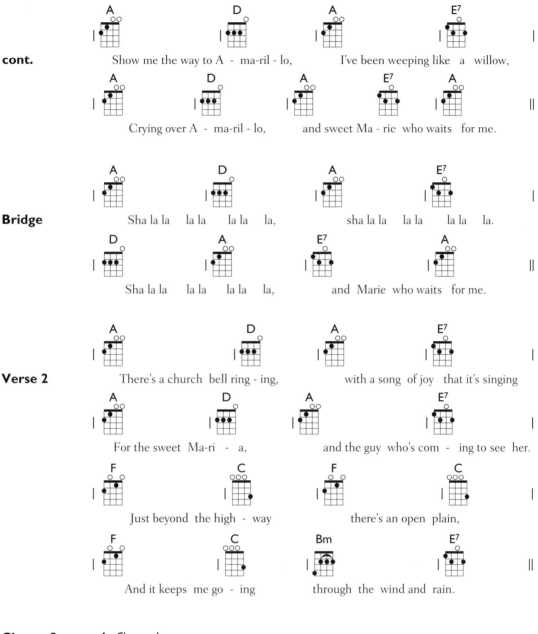

cont.   Show me the way to A - ma-ril - lo,   I've been weeping like a willow,

Crying over A - ma-ril - lo,   and sweet Ma - rie who waits for me.

Bridge   Sha la la   la la   la la   la,   sha la la   la la   la la   la.

Sha la la   la la   la la   la,   and Marie who waits for me.

Verse 2   There's a church bell ring - ing,   with a song of joy that it's singing

For the sweet Ma-ri - a,   and the guy who's com - ing to see her.

Just beyond the high - way   there's an open plain,

And it keeps me go - ing   through the wind and rain.

Chorus 2   *As Chorus 1*

Outro   *As Bridge - play x 3 and fade*

Trad.

KNEES UP MOTHER BROWN

Words and Music by Harris Weston and Bert Lee

Verses

1. There came a girl from France   who didn't know how to dance,
2. Oh,   hopping on one foot,   hopping on one foot,
3. Oh,   prancing up and down,   prancing up and down,
4. And   whirling round and round,   whirling round and round,

The   only thing that she could do was   knees up Mother Brown.
Hopping, hopping, never stopping, hopping on one foot.
Prancing, prancing, never dancing, prancing up and down.
Whirling, whirling, never twirling,   whirling round and round.

Chorus

Oh,   knees up Mother Brown,   knees up Mother Brown,

knees up, knees up, never let the breeze up, knees up Mother Brown.

KUM BA YAH

Traditional

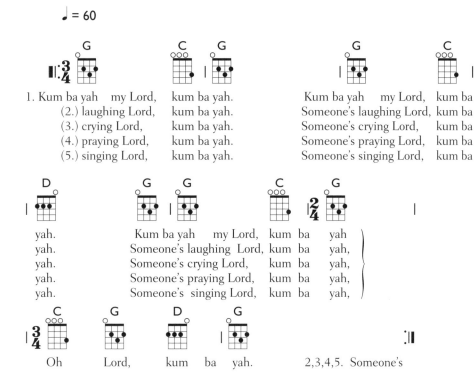

Verses

♩ = 60

|| G | C G | G | C |

1. Kum ba yah   my Lord,   kum ba yah.   Kum ba yah   my Lord,   kum ba
(2.) laughing Lord,   kum ba yah.   Someone's laughing Lord,   kum ba
(3.) crying Lord,   kum ba yah.   Someone's crying Lord,   kum ba
(4.) praying Lord,   kum ba yah.   Someone's praying Lord,   kum ba
(5.) singing Lord,   kum ba yah.   Someone's singing Lord,   kum ba

| D | G G | C 2/4 G |

yah.   Kum ba yah   my Lord,   kum ba   yah
yah.   Someone's laughing Lord,   kum ba   yah,
yah.   Someone's crying Lord,   kum ba   yah,
yah.   Someone's praying Lord,   kum ba   yah,
yah.   Someone's singing Lord,   kum ba   yah,

| 3/4 C G | D | G :||

Oh   Lord,   kum   ba   yah.   2,3,4,5. Someone's

LITTLE BROWN JUG

Words and Music by Joseph Winner

$\quad$ = 100

Verses

G   C   D⁷   G

Me and my wife live all a-lone in a little log hut we call our own.

G   C   D⁷   G

She loves gin and I love rum, and don't we have a lot of fun!

Chorus

G   C   D⁷   G

Ha, ha, ha,   you and me,   Little brown jug, don't I love thee!

G   C   D⁷   G

Ha, ha, ha,   you and me,   Little brown jug, don't I love thee!

Verse 2

When I go toiling on the farm
I take the little jug under my arm
Place it under a shady tree
Little brown jug, 'tis you and me

Verse 3

'Tis you that makes me friends and foes
'Tis you that makes me wear old clothes
But, seeing you're so near my nose
Tip her up and down she goes

Verse 4

If all the folks in Adam's race
Were gathered together in one place
I'd let them go without a tear
Before I'd part from you, my dear

Verse 5

If I'd a cow that gave such milk
I'd dress her in the finest silk
Feed her up on oats and hay
And milk her twenty times a day

Verse 6

I bought a cow from Farmer Jones
And she was nothing but skin and bones
I fed her up as fine as silk
She jumped the fence and strained her milk

Verse 7

And when I die don't bury me at all
Just pickle my bones in alcohol
Put a bottle o' booze at my head and feet
And then I know that I will keep...

Verse 8

The rose is red, my nose is too
The violet's blue and so are you
And yet, I guess, before I stop
We'd better take another drop

ROCK AROUND THE CLOCK

Words and Music by Jimmy De Knight and Max C Freedman

♩ = 175

Intro

A   A   A

One, two, three o'clock, four o'clock rock.   Five, six, seven o'clock,

A   A   A

eight o'clock rock.   Nine, ten, eleven o'clock,   twelve o'clock rock.

E⁷   E⁷

We're gonna rock   around   the clock tonight.

Verse 1

A   A   A

Put your glad rags on and join me hon',   we'll have some fun when the

A   D⁷   D⁷

clock strikes one. We're gonna rock   around   the clock tonight, we're gonna

A   A   E⁷

rock, rock, rock 'til the broad daylight. We're gonna rock, gonna rock

E⁷   A   A

a - round   the clock   to - night.

Verse 2

A   A   A

When the band strikes two,   three and four, if the band slows down we'll

A   D⁷   D⁷

yell for more. We're gonna rock   around   the   clock tonight, we're gonna

A   A   E⁷

rock, rock, rock 'til the broad daylight. We're gonna rock, gonna rock

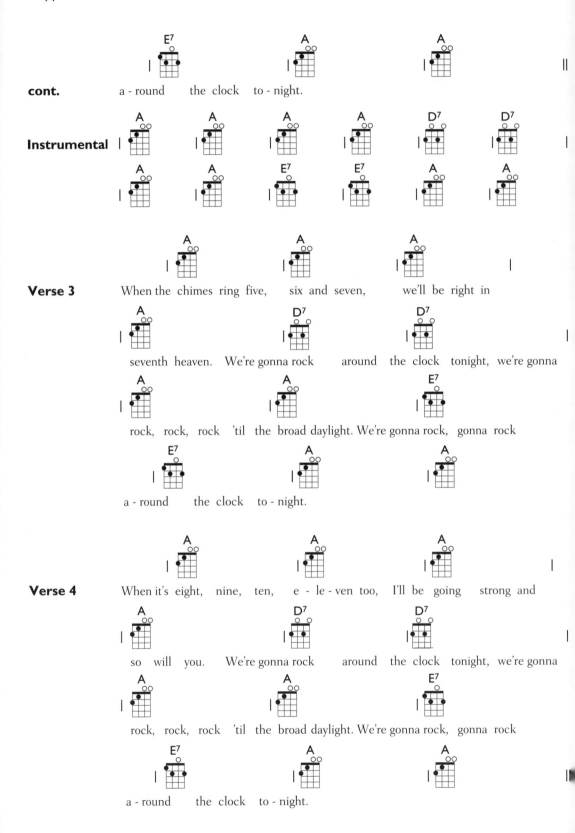

Instrumental 2 *As Instrumental 1*

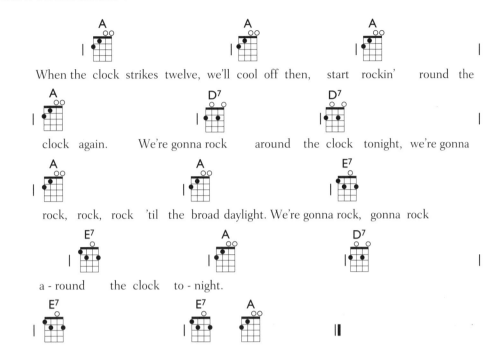

Verse 5

When the clock strikes twelve, we'll cool off then, start rockin' round the

clock again. We're gonna rock around the clock tonight, we're gonna

rock, rock, rock 'til the broad daylight. We're gonna rock, gonna rock

a - round the clock to - night.

Trad.

MY GRANDFATHER'S CLOCK

Words and Music by Henry Clay Work

♩ = 110

Verses

D	A	D	G

1. My   grand - father's   clock   was   too   large   for   the   shelf,   so   it
2. In   watch - ing   its   pendulum   swing   to   and   fro,   many

D	A	D

stood   nine - ty   years   on   the   floor.   It   was
years   had   he   spent   while   a   boy.   And   in

D	A	D	G

tal - ler   by   half   than   the   old   man   him - self,   though   it
child - hood   and   man - hood   the   clock   seemed   to   know   and   to

D	A	D

weighed   not   a   pen - ny - weight   more.   It   was
share   both   his   grief   and   his   joy.   For   it

D	G	D

bought   on   the   morn   of   the   day   that   he   was   born,   and   was
struck   twenty - four   when   he   entered   at   the   door,   with   a

D	A

al - ways   his   trea - sure   and   pride. ⎫
bloom - ing   and   beau - ti - ful   bride, ⎬   But   it

D	A	D	G

stopped,   short,   ne - ver   to   go   a - gain   when   the

D	A	D

old   man   died.

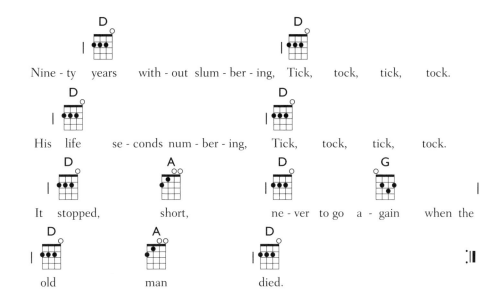

Chorus

Nine - ty years with - out slum - ber - ing, Tick, tock, tick, tock.

His life se - conds num - ber - ing, Tick, tock, tick, tock.

It stopped, short, ne - ver to go a - gain when the

old man died.

Verse 3

My grandfather said that of those he could hire
Not a servant so faithful he found.
For it wasted no time and had but one desire
At the close of each week to be wound.
And it kept in its place, not a frown upon its face
And its hand never hung by its side,
But it stopped, short, never to go again
When the old man died.

Verse 4

It rang an alarm in the dead of the night
An alarm that for years had been dumb,
And we knew that his spirit was pluming for flight
That his hour of departure had come.
Still the clock kept the time with a soft and muffled chime
As we silently stood by his side,
But it stopped, short, never to go again
When the old man died.

PROUD MARY

Words and Music by John Fogerty

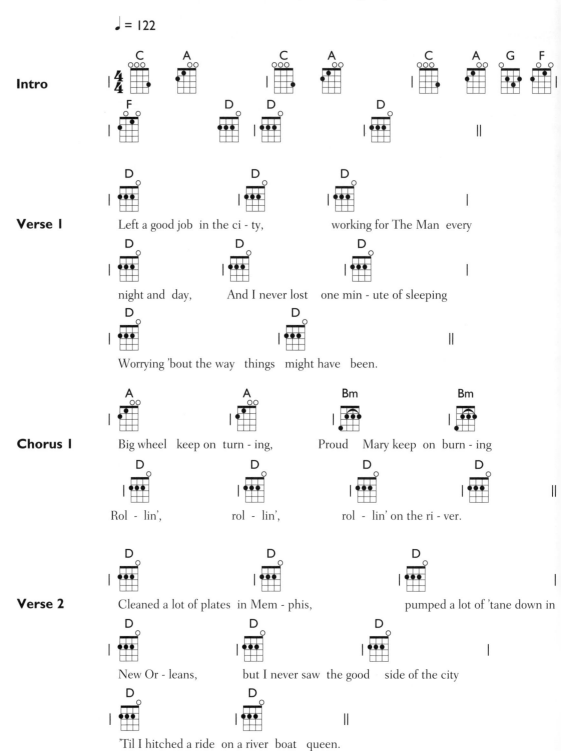

Intro

Verse 1

Left a good job in the ci - ty,   working for The Man every

night and day,   And I never lost   one min - ute of sleeping

Worrying 'bout the way   things   might have   been.

Chorus 1

Big wheel   keep on   turn - ing,   Proud   Mary keep on   burn - ing

Rol - lin',   rol - lin',   rol - lin' on the ri - ver.

Verse 2

Cleaned a lot of plates in Mem - phis,   pumped a lot of 'tane down in

New Or - leans,   but I never saw the good   side of the city

'Til I hitched a ride on a river boat   queen.

Chorus 2   *As Chorus 1*

Bridge 1   *As Intro 1*

Instrumental | D | D | D | D | D | D |

| D | D | A | A | Bm | Bm |

Mid-Section | D | D | D | D ||

Rol - lin',   rol - lin',   rol - lin' on the ri - ver.

Bridge 2   *As Intro 1*

Verse 3

| D | D | D |

If you come down to the ri - ver   bet you gonna find some

| D | D | D |

peo - ple who live.   You don't have to worry, 'cause you have no money,

| D | D ||

People on the river are hap - py to give.

Chorus 3   *As Chorus 1*

Outro   *As Mid-Section - repeat and fade*

SHAKE, RATTLE AND ROLL

Words and Music by Charles Calhoun

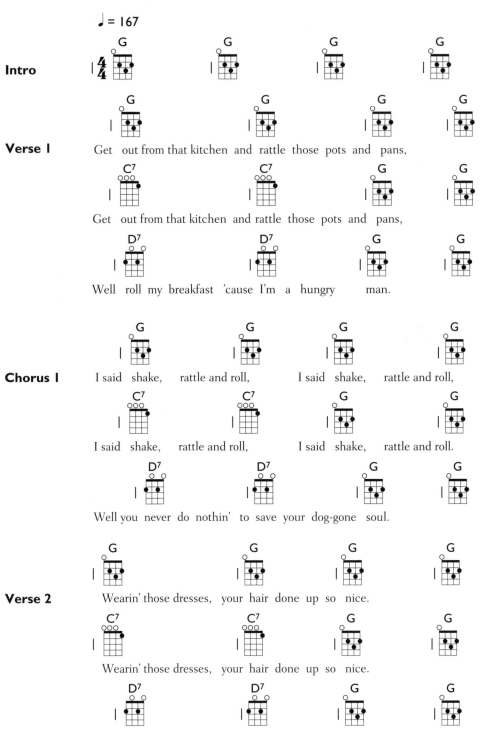

♩ = 167

Intro

Verse 1

Get out from that kitchen and rattle those pots and pans,

Get out from that kitchen and rattle those pots and pans,

Well roll my breakfast 'cause I'm a hungry man.

Chorus 1

I said shake, rattle and roll, I said shake, rattle and roll,

I said shake, rattle and roll, I said shake, rattle and roll.

Well you never do nothin' to save your dog-gone soul.

Verse 2

Wearin' those dresses, your hair done up so nice.

Wearin' those dresses, your hair done up so nice.

You look so warm but your heart is cold as ice.

Chorus 2   *As Chorus 1*

Solo   Go!   Go!

Go!   Go!

Go!

Verse 3   I'm like a one-eyed cat, peep - in' in a seafood store,

I'm like a one-eyed cat, peep - in' in a seafood store,

I can look at you 'til you don't love me no more.

Verse 4   I be - lieve you're doin' me wrong and now I know,

I be - lieve you're doin' me wrong and now I know.

The more I work, the faster my money goes.

Chorus 3   *As Chorus 1*

Shake, rattle and roll!

IT'S IN HIS KISS
(THE SHOOP SHOOP SONG)
Words and Music by Rudy Clark

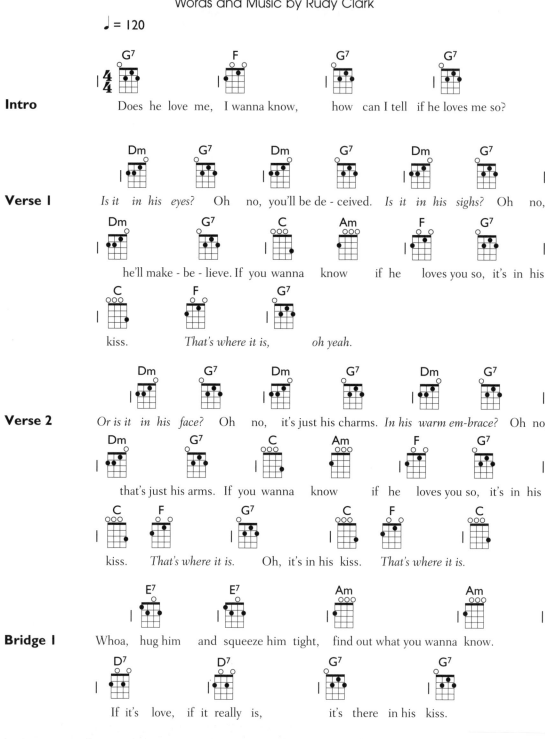

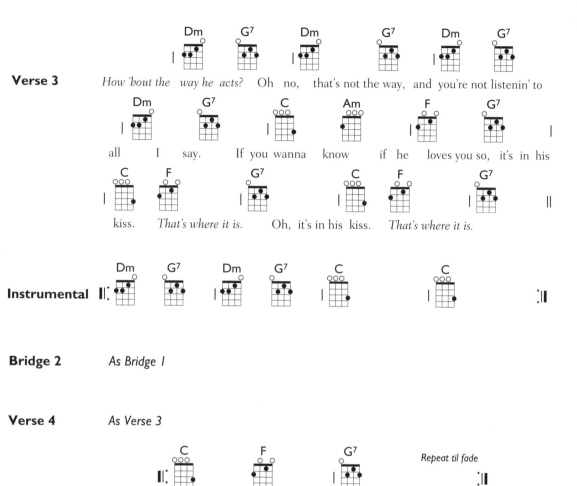

Verse 3

How 'bout the way he acts? Oh no, that's not the way, and you're not listenin' to
all I say. If you wanna know if he loves you so, it's in his
kiss. *That's where it is.* Oh, it's in his kiss. *That's where it is.*

Instrumental

Bridge 2   As Bridge 1

Verse 4   As Verse 3

Repeat til fade

Outro   It's in his kiss. *That's where it is.* It's in his

Trad.

THE SKYE BOAT SONG

Words by Harold Boulton

Music Traditional

♩ = 70

Chorus

 C G C F C   G

Speed bonnie boat, like a bird on the wing, onward, the sai - lors cry.

 C G C F C

Car-ry the lad that's born to be King   over the sea to Skye.

Verses

 Am Dm Am F Am

1. Loud the winds howl, loud the waves roar, thunderclaps rend the air.
2. Though the waves leap, soft shall ye sleep, ocean's a roy - al bed,
3. Many's the lad   fought on that day, well the Claymore could wield,
4. Burned are their homes, exile and death,   scatter the loy - al men.

 Am Dm Am F G

Baffled, our foes   stand by the shore, follow they will not dare.
Racked in the deep, Flora will keep watch by your weary head.
When the night came, silently lay dead in Culloden's field.
Yet ere the sword   cool in the sheath Charlie will come a - gain.

SLOOP JOHN B

Words and Music by Brian Wilson

♩ = 125

Verses

C	C	C	C

1. We come on the sloop John B,   my grand - father and me.
2. The first mate he got drunk,   and broke in the Captain's trunk
3. The poor cook he got the fits   and threw away all my grits

C	C	G7	G7

A - round Nas - sau Town   we did roam.   Drinking all
The constable had to come   and take him away.   Sheriff John
And then he took and he ate   all of my corn.   Let me go

C	C	F	Dm

night,   got in - to a fight.   Well I
Stone,   why don't you leave me alone?   Well I
home,   why don't they let me go home?   This is the

C	G7	C	C

feel so broke up,   I wan - na go home.
feel so broke up,   I wan - na go home.
worst trip   I've ever been on.

Chorus

C	C	C	C

So hoist up the John B's sail,   see how the main sail sets.

C	C	G7	G7

Call for the Captain a - shore, let me go home.   Let me go

C	C	F	Dm

home,   I wan - na go home,   yeah yeah.   Well I

C	G7	C	C

feel so broke up,   I wan - na go home.

OVER THE RAINBOW
(FROM "THE WIZARD OF OZ")

Lyrics by E Y Harburg
Music by Harold Arlen

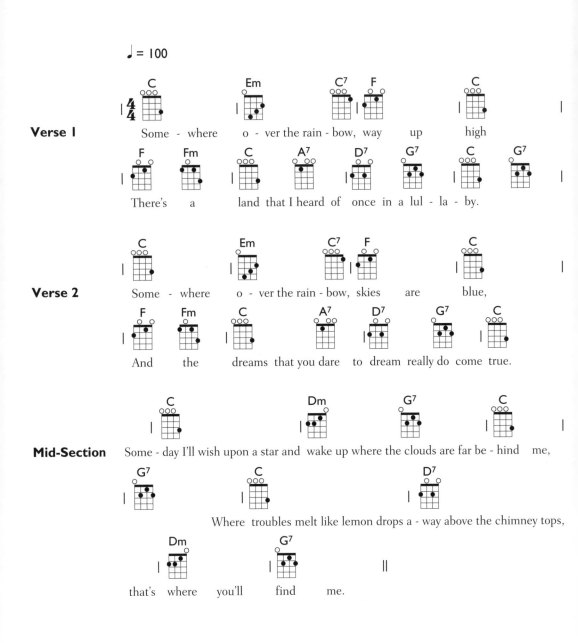

♩ = 100

Verse 1

C — Em — C⁷ F — C

Some - where   o - ver the rain - bow, way   up   high

F Fm — C A⁷ — D⁷ — G⁷ — C — G⁷

There's   a   land that I heard of once in a lul - la - by.

Verse 2

C — Em — C⁷ F — C

Some - where   o - ver the rain - bow, skies   are   blue,

F Fm — C — A⁷ — D⁷ — G⁷ — C

And   the   dreams that you dare to dream really do come true.

Mid-Section

C — Dm — G⁷ — C

Some - day I'll wish upon a star and wake up where the clouds are far be - hind   me,

G⁷ — C — D⁷

Where troubles melt like lemon drops a - way above the chimney tops,

Dm — G⁷

that's   where   you'll   find   me.

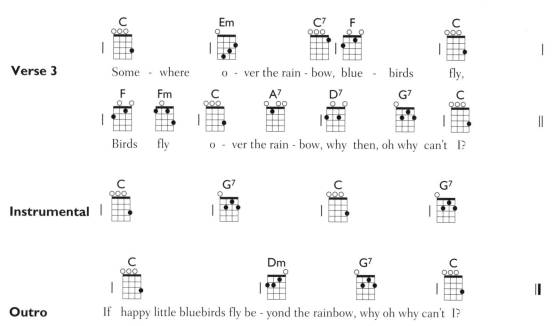

Verse 3 Some - where   o - ver the rain - bow, blue - birds   fly,

Birds   fly   o - ver the rain - bow, why then, oh why can't I?

Instrumental

Outro   If happy little bluebirds fly be - yond the rainbow, why oh why can't I?

SUPERCALIFRAGILISTICEXPIALIDOCIOUS
(FROM "MARY POPPINS")

Words and Music by Richard Sherman and Robert Sherman

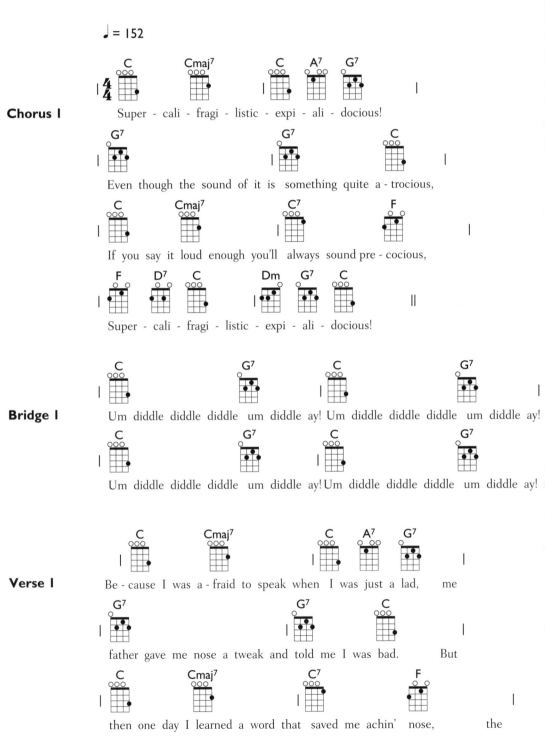

Chorus 1

Super - cali - fragi - listic - expi - ali - docious!

Even though the sound of it is something quite a - trocious,

If you say it loud enough you'll always sound pre - cocious,

Super - cali - fragi - listic - expi - ali - docious!

Bridge 1

Um diddle diddle diddle um diddle ay! Um diddle diddle diddle um diddle ay!

Um diddle diddle diddle um diddle ay! Um diddle diddle diddle um diddle ay!

Verse 1

Be - cause I was a - fraid to speak when I was just a lad, me

father gave me nose a tweak and told me I was bad. But

then one day I learned a word that saved me achin' nose, the

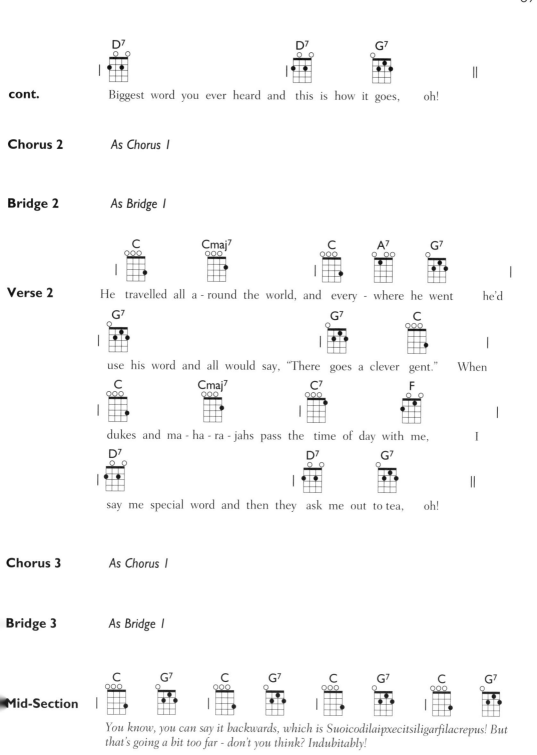

cont. Biggest word you ever heard and this is how it goes, oh!

Chorus 2 *As Chorus 1*

Bridge 2 *As Bridge 1*

Verse 2 He travelled all a - round the world, and every - where he went he'd
use his word and all would say, "There goes a clever gent." When
dukes and ma - ha - ra - jahs pass the time of day with me, I
say me special word and then they ask me out to tea, oh!

Chorus 3 *As Chorus 1*

Bridge 3 *As Bridge 1*

Mid-Section *You know, you can say it backwards, which is Suoicodilaipxecitsiligarfilacrepus! But that's going a bit too far - don't you think? Indubitably!*

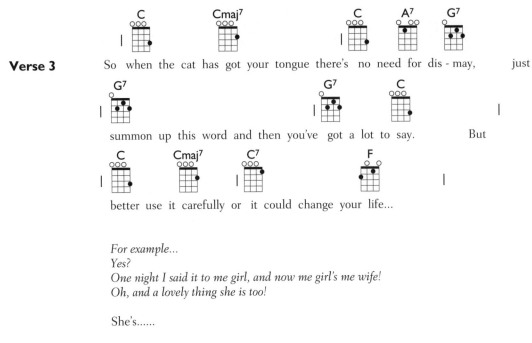

Verse 3   So when the cat has got your tongue there's no need for dis - may,   just

summon up this word and then you've got a lot to say.   But

better use it carefully or it could change your life...

For example...
Yes?
One night I said it to me girl, and now me girl's me wife!
Oh, and a lovely thing she is too!

She's......

Chorus 4   *As Chorus 1*

Outro

THIS OLD MAN

Traditional

♩ = 115

Verses

D   G   A

1. This old man,   he played one,   he played knick-knack on my thumb,
2. This old man,   he played two,   he played knick-knack on my shoe,
3. This old man,   he played three,   he played knick-knack on my knee,
4. This old man,   he played four,   he played knick-knack on my door,
5. This old man,   he played five,   he played knick-knack on my hive,
6. This old man,   he played six,   he played knick-knack with some sticks,

Chorus

D

With a knick-knack, paddy whack, give a dog a bone,

A   D

This old man came rolling home.

Verse 7

This old man, he played seven,
He played knick-knack up in Heaven,

Verse 8

This old man, he played eight,
He played knick-knack on my gate,

Verse 9

This old man, he played nine,
He played knick-knack on my spine,

Verse 10

This old man, he played ten,
He played knick-knack once again,

WHEN I'M CLEANING WINDOWS

Words and Music by Harry Gifford, Fred E Cliffe and George Formby

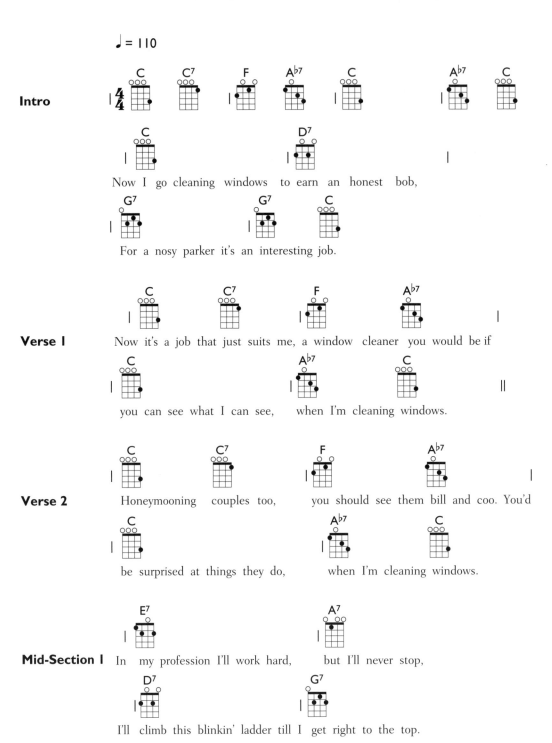

♩ = 110

Intro

C   C7   F   Ab7   C   Ab7   C

C   D7

Now I go cleaning windows to earn an honest bob,

G7   G7   C

For a nosy parker it's an interesting job.

Verse 1

C   C7   F   Ab7

Now it's a job that just suits me, a window cleaner you would be if

C   Ab7   C

you can see what I can see,   when I'm cleaning windows.

Verse 2

C   C7   F   Ab7

Honeymooning   couples too,   you should see them bill and coo. You'd

C   Ab7   C

be surprised at things they do,   when I'm cleaning windows.

Mid-Section 1

E7   A7

In   my profession I'll work hard,   but I'll never stop,

D7   G7

I'll   climb this blinkin' ladder till I get right to the top.

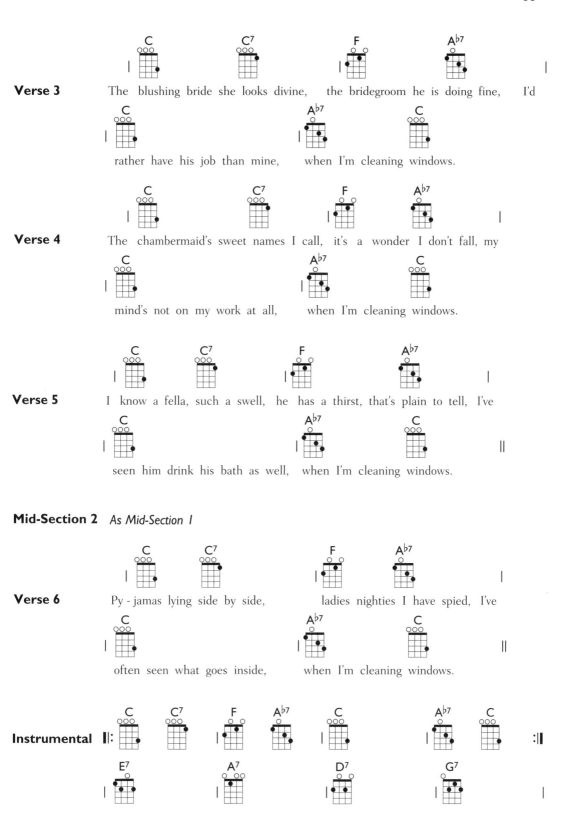

Verse 3

C   C⁷   F   A♭⁷

The blushing bride she looks divine, the bridegroom he is doing fine, I'd

C   A♭⁷   C

rather have his job than mine, when I'm cleaning windows.

Verse 4

C   C⁷   F   A♭⁷

The chambermaid's sweet names I call, it's a wonder I don't fall, my

C   A♭⁷   C

mind's not on my work at all, when I'm cleaning windows.

Verse 5

C   C⁷   F   A♭⁷

I know a fella, such a swell, he has a thirst, that's plain to tell, I've

C   A♭⁷   C

seen him drink his bath as well, when I'm cleaning windows.

Mid-Section 2 *As Mid-Section 1*

Verse 6

C   C⁷   F   A♭⁷

Py - jamas lying side by side, ladies nighties I have spied, I've

C   A♭⁷   C

often seen what goes inside, when I'm cleaning windows.

Instrumental

C   C⁷   F   A♭⁷   C   A♭⁷   C

E⁷   A⁷   D⁷   G⁷

cont.

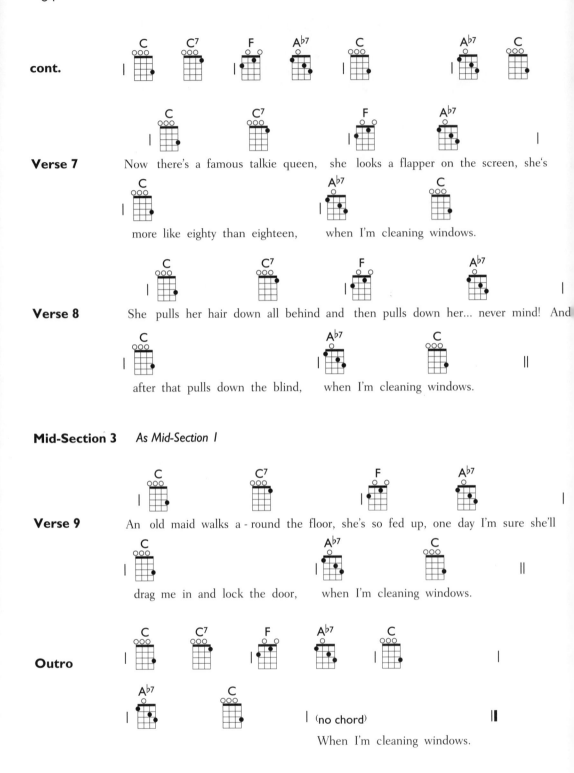

Verse 7
Now there's a famous talkie queen, she looks a flapper on the screen, she's
more like eighty than eighteen, when I'm cleaning windows.

Verse 8
She pulls her hair down all behind and then pulls down her... never mind! And
after that pulls down the blind, when I'm cleaning windows.

Mid-Section 3   *As Mid-Section I*

Verse 9
An old maid walks a - round the floor, she's so fed up, one day I'm sure she'll
drag me in and lock the door, when I'm cleaning windows.

Outro

(no chord)
When I'm cleaning windows.

WHEN THE SAINTS GO MARCHING IN

Traditional

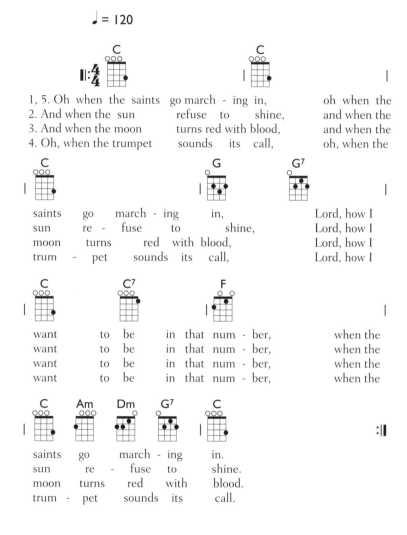

Verses

♩ = 120

1, 5. Oh when the saints go march - ing in, oh when the
2. And when the sun refuse to shine, and when the
3. And when the moon turns red with blood, and when the
4. Oh, when the trumpet sounds its call, oh, when the

saints go march - ing in, Lord, how I
sun re - fuse to shine, Lord, how I
moon turns red with blood, Lord, how I
trum - pet sounds its call, Lord, how I

want to be in that num - ber, when the
want to be in that num - ber, when the
want to be in that num - ber, when the
want to be in that num - ber, when the

saints go march - ing in.
sun re - fuse to shine.
moon turns red with blood.
trum - pet sounds its call.

WHISKEY IN THE JAR

Words and Music by Barney MacKenna, Ciaran Bourke, John Sheahan, Luke Kelley and Ronnie Drew

♩ = 105

Verses

1. As   I was going over the far famed Kerry mountains, I
2. I   counted out his money and it made a pretty penny, I
3. I   went up to my chamber, all for to take a slumber,   I
4. 'Twas early in the morning, just before I rose to travel,   up

met with Captain Farrell and his money he was counting, I
put it in me pocket,   and I took it home to Jenny.   She
dreamt of gold and jewels and for sure it was no wonder, but
comes a band of footmen and like - wise Captain Farrell.   I

first produced me pistol and I then produced me rapier, saying
sighed and she swore that she never would deceive me, but the
Jenny drew me charges, and she filled them up with water, then
first produced me pistol for she'd stolen away me rapier, I

"Stand and de - liver" for he were a bold deceiver. ⎞
devil   take the women for they never can be easy. ⎟
sent   for Captain Farrell to be ready for the slaughter. ⎟
couldn't shoot the water, so a prisoner I was taken. ⎠

Chorus   Mu - sha ring dumma doo damma daa.   Whack fall the daddy - O',

Whack fall the daddy - O', there's whiskey in the jar.

Verse 5

Now there's some take delight in the carriages a rolling
And others take delight in the hurling and the bowling
But I take delight in the juice of the barley
And courting pretty fair maids in the morning bright and early

Verse 6

If anyone can aid me 'tis my brother in the Army
If I can find his station in Cork or Killarney
And if he'll go with me, we'll go rovin' in Killkenny
And I'm sure he'll treat me better than my own a-sporting Jenny

Y VIVA ESPAÑA

Words and Music by Leo Caerts
Original Words by Leo Rozenstraeten
English Words by Eddie Seago

♩ = 130

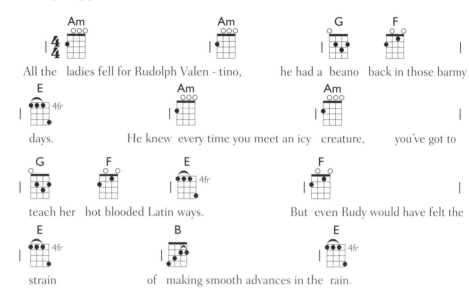

Verses

All the ladies fell for Rudolph Valen - tino, he had a beano back in those barmy days. He knew every time you meet an icy creature, you've got to teach her hot blooded Latin ways. But even Rudy would have felt the strain of making smooth advances in the rain.

Chorus

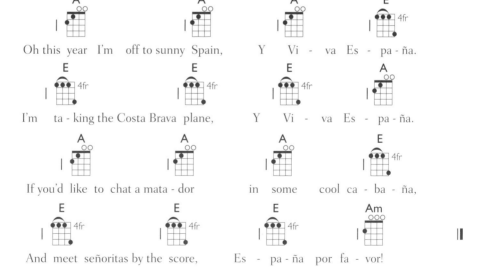

Oh this year I'm off to sunny Spain, Y Vi - va Es - pa - ña. I'm ta - king the Costa Brava plane, Y Vi - va Es - pa - ña. If you'd like to chat a mata - dor in some cool ca - ba - ña, And meet señoritas by the score, Es - pa - ña por fa - vor!

Verse 2

Quite by chance to hot romance I found the answer
Flamenco dancers are by far the finest bet
There was one who whispered, "oh hasta la vista"
Each time I kissed him behind the castanette
He rattled his maracas close to me
In no time I was trembling at the knee

Verse 3

When they first arrive the girls are pink and pasty
But oh so tasty as soon as they go brown
I guess they know every fellow will be queuing
To do the wooing his girlfriend won't allow
But every dog must have his lucky day
That's why I've learnt the way to shout, "Olé!"

Trad.

YANKEE DOODLE

Traditional

♩ = 135

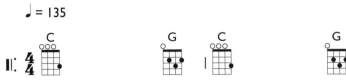

Verses

1. Yankee Doodle went to town a - riding on a po - ny,
2. Father and I went down to camp along with Captain Gooding,
3. And there was Captain Washington, and gentle folks around him,

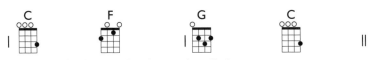

He stuck a feather in his hat and called it ma - ca - ro - ni.
And there we saw the men and boys as thick as hasty pudding.
They say he's growing so tamal proud, he will not right without him.

Chorus

Yankee Doodle keep it up,   Yankee Doodle dan - dy.

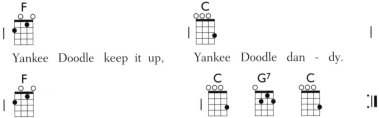

Mind the music and the step and with the girls be han - dy.

The Ukulele playlist. Yellow book
ISBN10: 0-571-53328-0
EAN13: 978-0-571-53328-2

Babooshka *Kate Bush* · **Bad Moon Rising** *Creedence Clearwater Revival* · **Beat It** *Michael Jackson*
The Beep Beep Song *Simone White* · **Boulevard Of Broken Dreams** *Green Day*
Breakfast At Tiffany's *Deep Blue Something* · **Crazy** *Gnarls Barkley*
Dani California *Red Hot Chili Peppers* · **Dream A Little Dream Of Me** *Mamas & Papas*
Fisherman's Blues *The Waterboys* · **The House Of The Rising Sun** *The Animals*
How Deep Is Your Love *The Bee Gees* · **Hush** *Deep Purple* · **I Don't Feel Like Dancin'** *Scissor Sisters*
I Wish *Stevie Wonder* · **King Of The Road** *Roger Miller* · **Life On Mars?** *David Bowie*
Like A Prayer *Madonna* · **Losing My Religion** *R.E.M.* · **Mamma Mia** *ABBA* · **Panic** *The Smiths*
Paranoid *Black Sabbath* · **Rehab** *Amy Winehouse* · **Ring Of Fire** *Johnny Cash* · **Rock Star** *Nickelback*
Signed, Sealed, Delivered *Stevie Wonder* · **Smells Like Teen Spirit** *Nirvana* · **Take On Me** *a-ha*
Toxic *Britney Spears* · **Wade In The Water** *Eva Cassidy*
Warwick Avenue *Duffy* · **Whatever You Want** *Status Quo*

To buy Faber Music publications or to find out about the full range of titles available
please contact your local music retailer or Faber Music sales enquiries:

Faber Music Ltd, Burnt Mill, Elizabeth Way, Harlow CM20 2HX
Tel: +44 (0) 1279 82 89 82   Fax: +44 (0) 1279 82 89 83
sales@fabermusic.com   fabermusic.com   expressprintmusic.com

The Ukulele playlist. Blue book
ISBN10: 0-571-53327-2
EAN13: 978-0-571-53327-5

Back For Good *Take That* · **Bittersweet Symphony** *The Verve* · **Build Me Up Buttercup** *The Foundations*
Come On Eileen *Dexy's Midnight Runners* · **Crazy Little Thing Called Love** *Queen* · **Creep** *Radiohead*
Daydream Believer *The Monkees* · **Don't Get Me Wrong** *The Pretenders*
Five Hundred Miles *Proclaimers* · **Flagpole Sitta** *Harvey Danger*
Fluorescent Adolescent *Arctic Monkeys* · **Foundations** *Kate Nash*
Go Your Own Way *Fleetwood Mac* · **Happy Together** *The Turtles* · **Hit The Road Jack** *Ray Charles*
Hotel California *Eagles* · **House Of Fun** *Madness* · **I Wanna Be Like You** *Jungle Book*
Isn't She Lovely *Stevie Wonder* · **Kids In America** *Kim Wilde* · **Last Nite** *The Strokes*
The Man Who Sold The World *Nirvana* · **Never Want To Say It's Love** *Dido*
Nutbush City Limits *Tina Turner* · **The Passenger** *Iggy Pop* · **Song 2** *Blur*
Sweet About Me *Gabriella Cilmi* · **That's Not My Name** *The Ting Tings*
Valerie *Mark Ronson feat Amy Winehouse* · **Wild Thing** *The Troggs* · **You're Beautiful** *James Blunt*

To buy Faber Music publications or to find out about the full range of titles available
please contact your local music retailer or Faber Music sales enquiries:

Faber Music Ltd, Burnt Mill, Elizabeth Way, Harlow CM20 2HX
Tel: +44 (0) 1279 82 89 82   Fax: +44 (0) 1279 82 89 83
sales@fabermusic.com   fabermusic.com   expressprintmusic.com

The Ukulele playlist. Christmas
ISBN10: 0-571-53358-2
EAN13: 978-0-571-53358-9

Angels From The Realms Of Glory · Auld Lang Syne · Away In A Manger · Blue Christmas
The Boar's Head Carol · The Christmas Song · Deck The Halls · Ding Dong Merrily On High
Do They Know It's Christmas? · Fairytale Of New York · Frosty The Snowman
Grandma Got Run Over By A Reindeer · Good King Wenceslas · Hark The Herald Angels Sing
Have Yourself A Merry Little Christmas · Here We Come A-Wassailing · The Holly And The Ivy
I Saw Mommy Kissing Santa Claus · I Wish It Could Be Christmas Everyday · In The Bleak Midwinter
Jingle Bells · Joy To The World · Last Christmas · The Little Drummer Boy · Merry Christmas Everyone
Merry Xmas Everybody · O Come All Ye Faithful · O Holy Night · Rockin' Around The Christmas Tree
Rudolph The Red Nosed Reindeer · Run Rudolph Run · Santa Claus Is Comin' To Town · Silent Night
Sleigh Ride · We Three Kings · We Wish You A Merry Christmas · When A Child Is Born
While Shepherds Watched Their Flocks · White Christmas

To buy Faber Music publications or to find out about the full range of titles available
please contact your local music retailer or Faber Music sales enquiries:

Faber Music Ltd, Burnt Mill, Elizabeth Way, Harlow CM20 2HX
Tel: +44 (0) 1279 82 89 82   Fax: +44 (0) 1279 82 89 83
sales@fabermusic.com   fabermusic.com   expressprintmusic.com